play guitar with...

foo fighters

Wise Publications
part of The Music Sales Group
London / New York / Paris / Sydney / Copenhagen / Berlin / Madrid / Tokyo

all my life

Words & Music by
Dave Grohl, Taylor Hawkins, Nate Mendel & Chris Shiflett

Full performance demo: CD track 1
Backing only: CD track 8

4

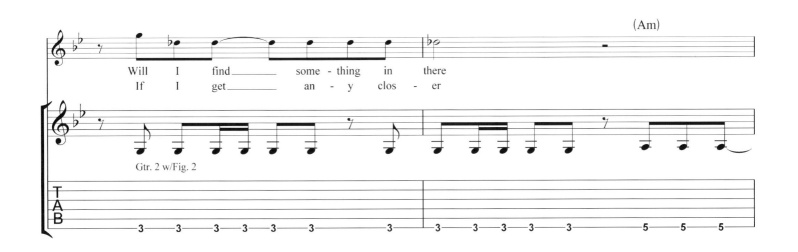

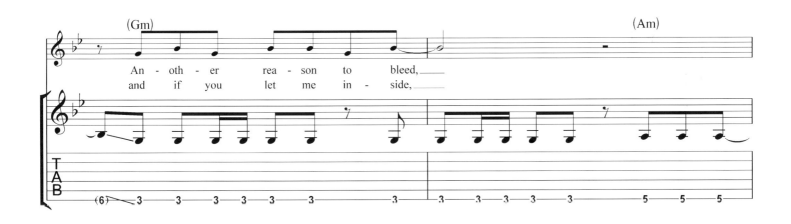

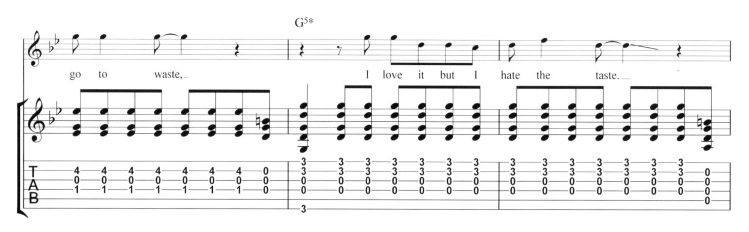

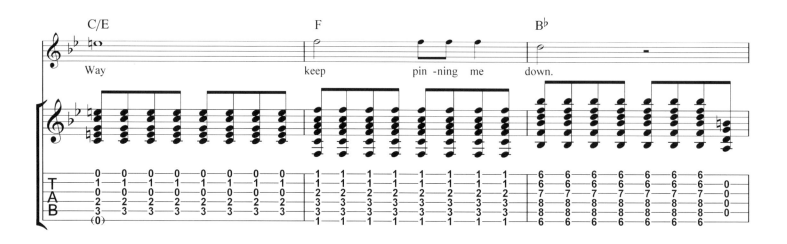

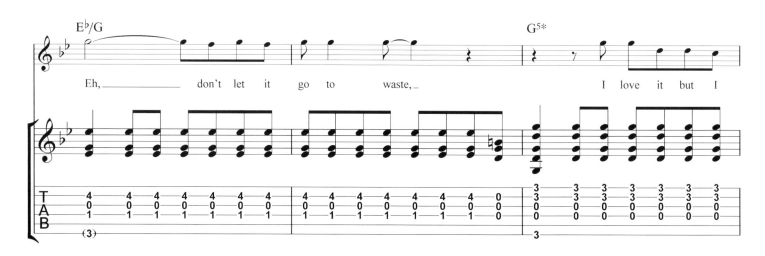

All my life I've been search-ing for some-thing, some - thing nev-er comes, nev-er leads to no-thing. No-

- thing sat-is-fies but I'm get-ting close, clos - er to the prize at the end of the rope.

All night long_ I dream_ of the day,_ when_ it comes a-round and it's tak-en a-way._ Leaves_

- me with the feel-ing that I feel the most, feel_ it come to life when I see your ghost. Then I'm

long road to ruin

Words & Music by
Dave Grohl, Taylor Hawkins, Nate Mendel & Chris Shiflett

Full performance demo: CD track 2
Backing only: CD track 9

Fsus²/C

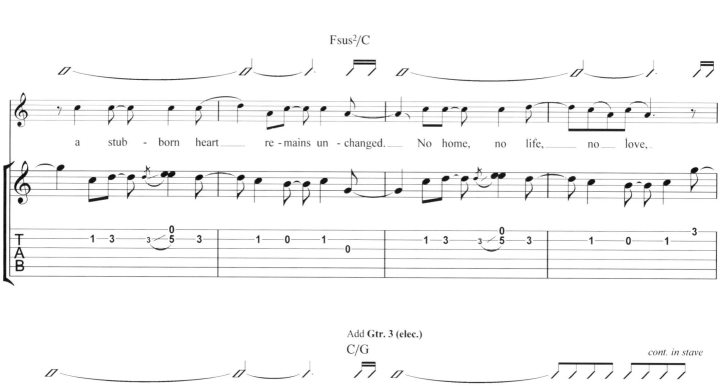

a stub - born heart___ re - mains un - changed.___ No home, no life,___ no love,___

Add **Gtr. 3 (elec.)**

C/G

cont. in stave

no stran - ger sing - ing___ in___ your___ name.___ It

Pre-chorus

(Fadd⁹)   (Gadd¹¹/B)   (Fadd⁹/C)   (Gadd¹¹/B)

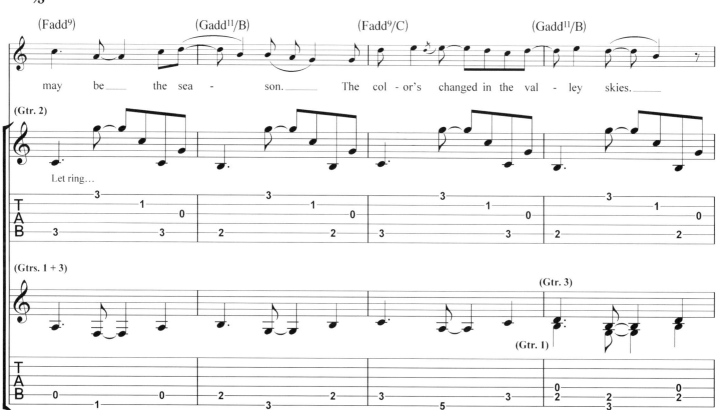

may be___ the sea - son.___ The col - or's changed in the val - ley skies.___

(Gtr. 2)

Let ring…

(Gtrs. 1 + 3)

(Gtr. 3)

(Gtr. 1)

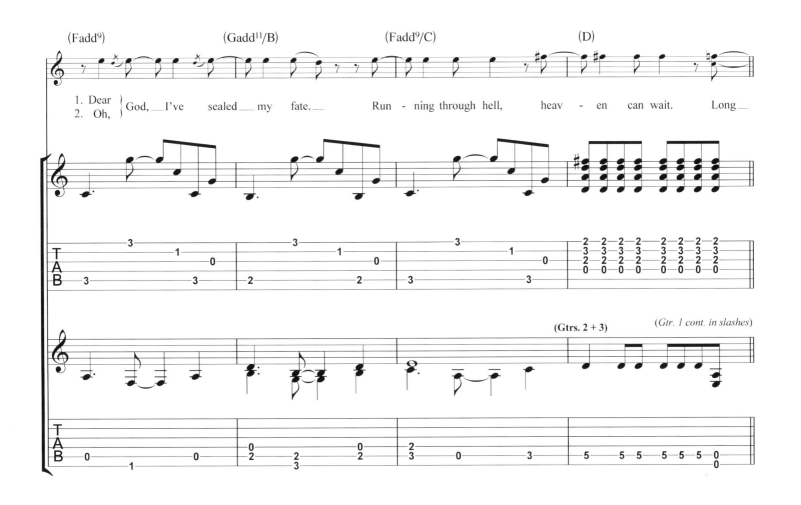

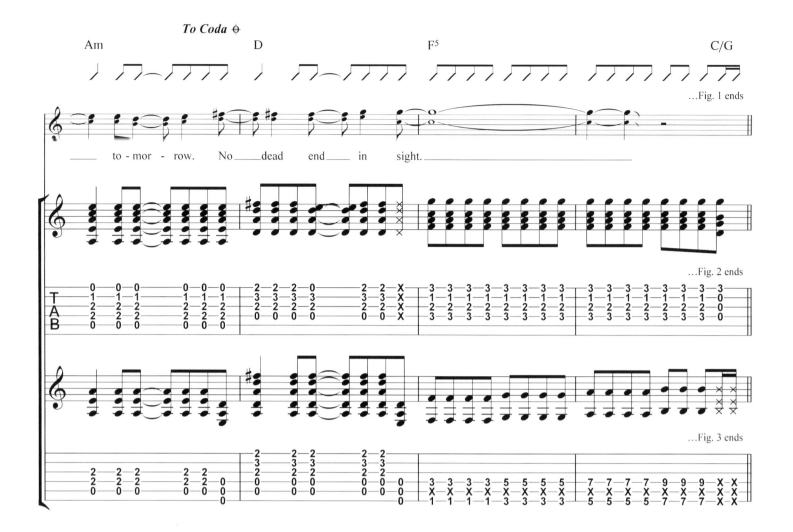

To Coda ⊕

Am   D   F5   C/G

...Fig. 1 ends

____ to - mor - row. No ____ dead end ____ in sight.____

...Fig. 2 ends

...Fig. 3 ends

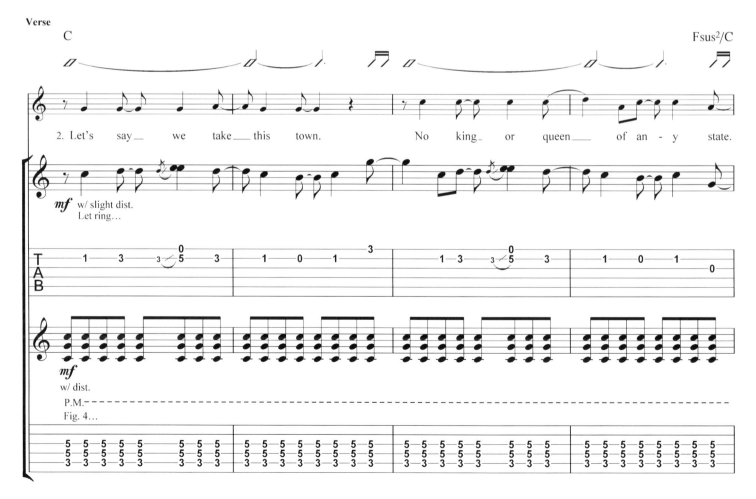

Verse

C   Fsus2/C

2. Let's say ____ we take ____ this town.   No king or queen ____ of an - y state.

mf w/ slight dist.
Let ring...

mf
w/ dist.
P.M. - - - - - - - - - - - - - - - -
Fig. 4...

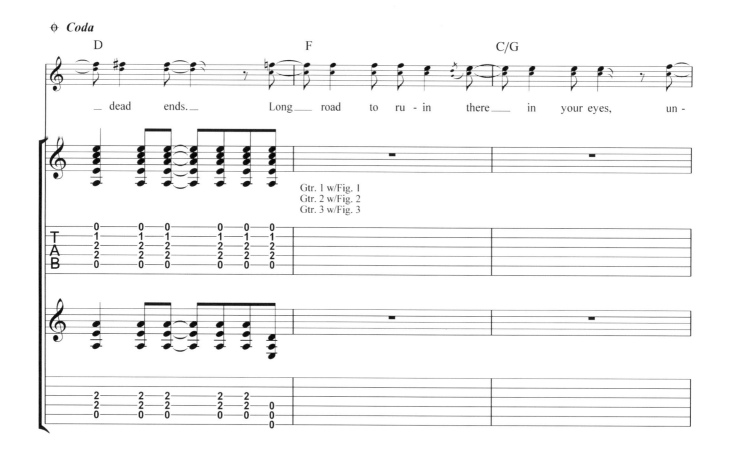

⊕ Coda

dead ends.___ Long___ road to ru - in there___ in your eyes, un -

Gtr. 1 w/Fig. 1
Gtr. 2 w/Fig. 2
Gtr. 3 w/Fig. 3

- der the cold street - lights.   No___ to - mor - row.   No___

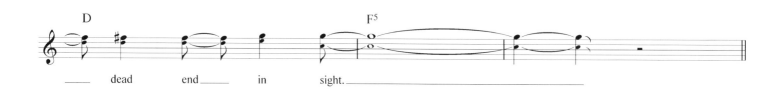

___ dead end___ in sight.___

Interlude

Let ring...
Fig. 4

cont. sim

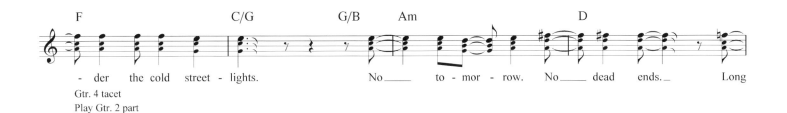

- der the cold street - lights. No ___ to - mor - row. No dead ends. ___ Long

Gtr. 4 tacet
Play Gtr. 2 part

___ road to ru - in there ___ in your eyes un - der the cold street - lights. No ___

___ to - mor - row. No ___ dead ends. ___ Long ___ road to ru - in there ___ in your eyes un -

- der the cold street - lights. No ___ to - mor - row. No ___ dead end in sight.

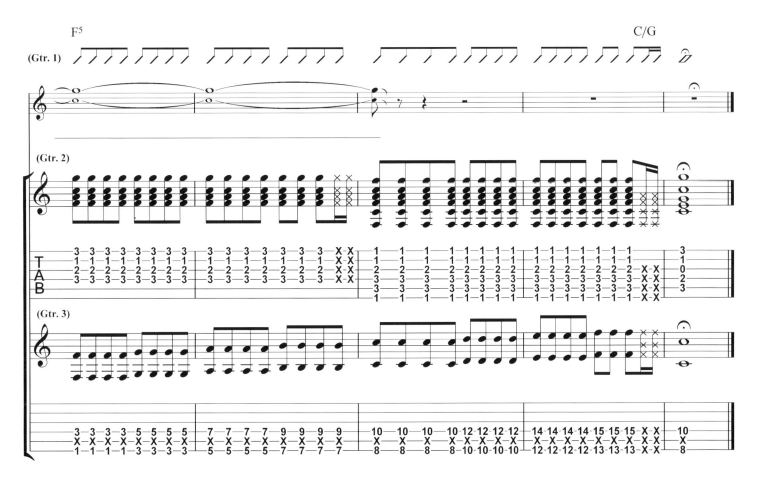

best of you

Words & Music by
Dave Grohl, Taylor Hawkins, Nate Mendel & Chris Shiflett

Full performance demo: CD track 3
Backing only: CD track 10

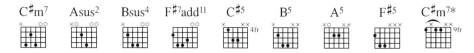

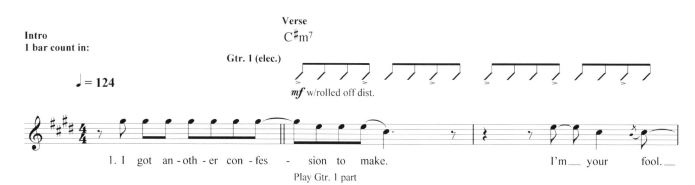

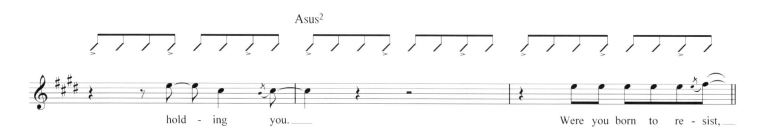

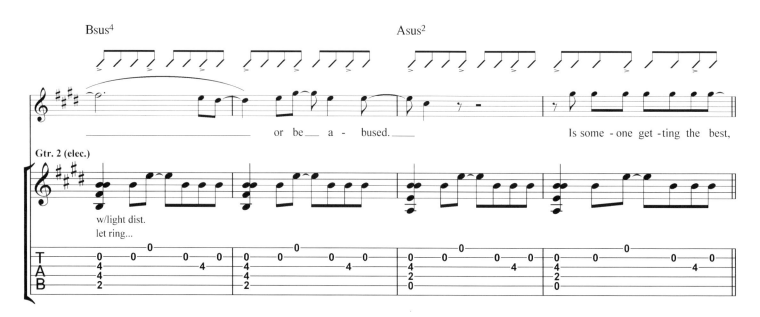

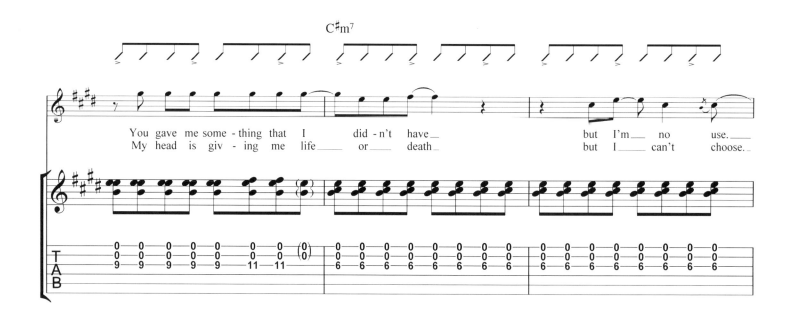

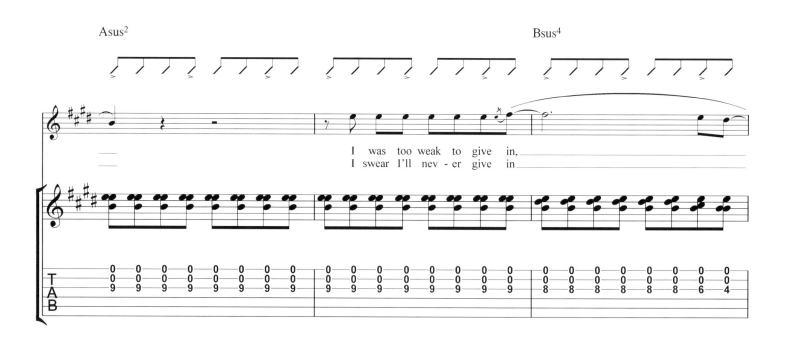

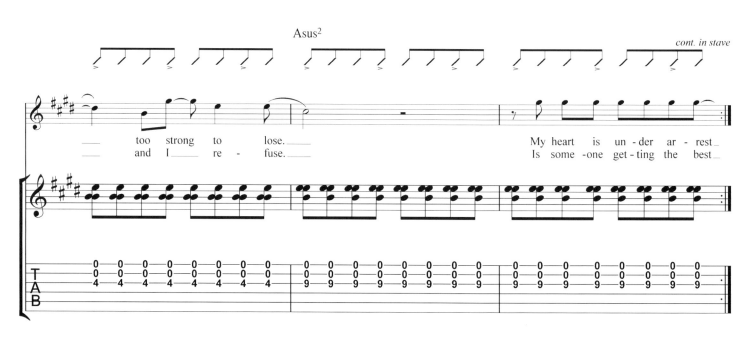

Chorus %

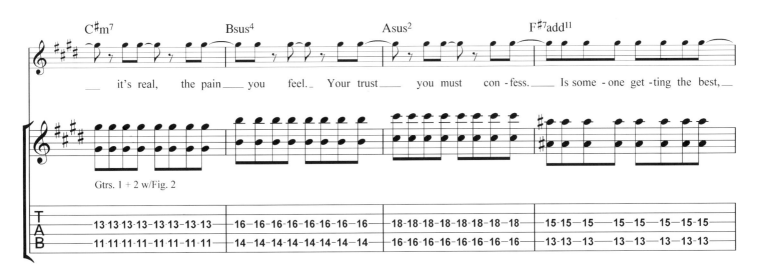

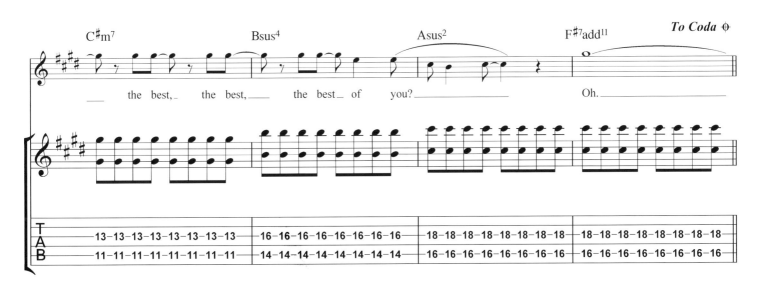

23

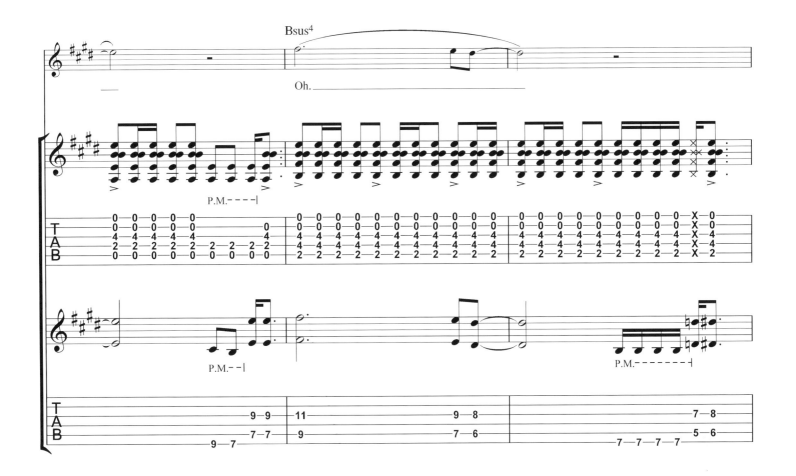

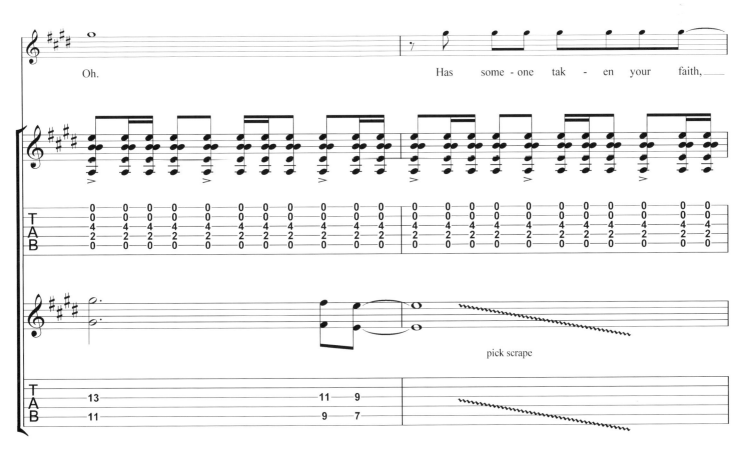

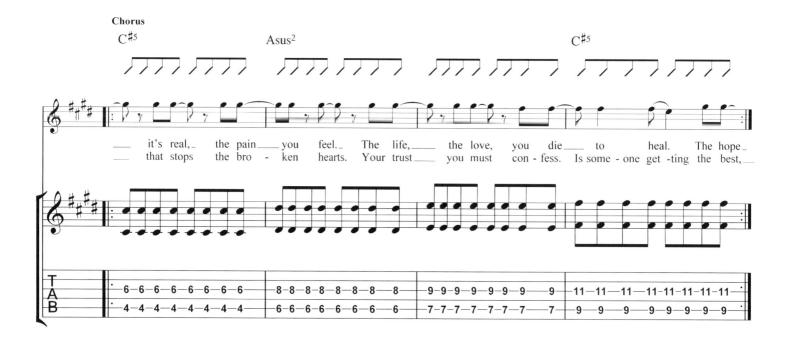

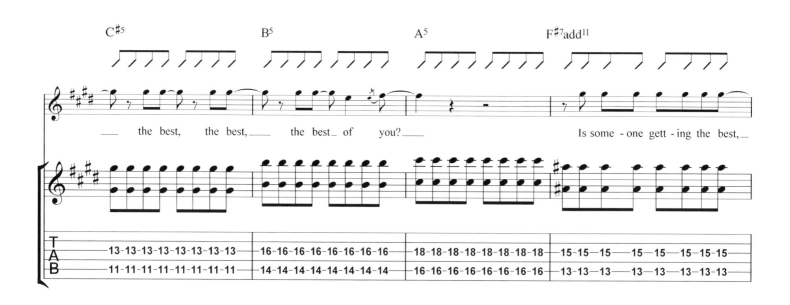

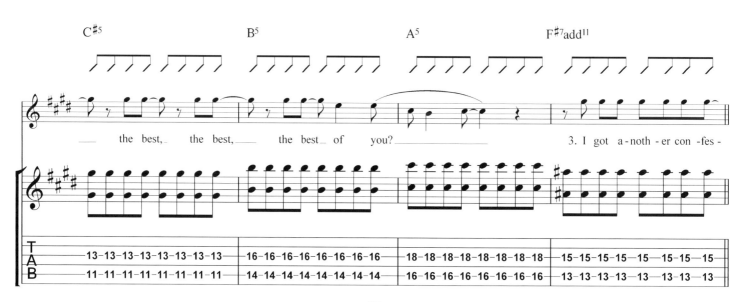

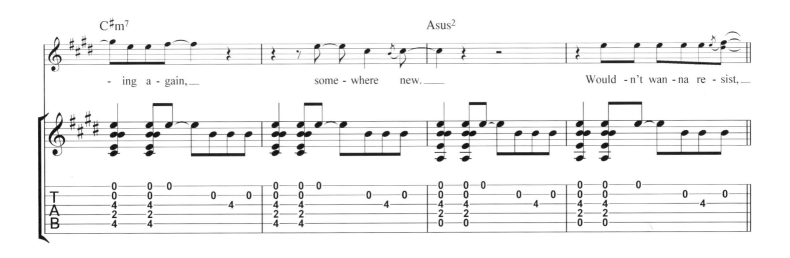

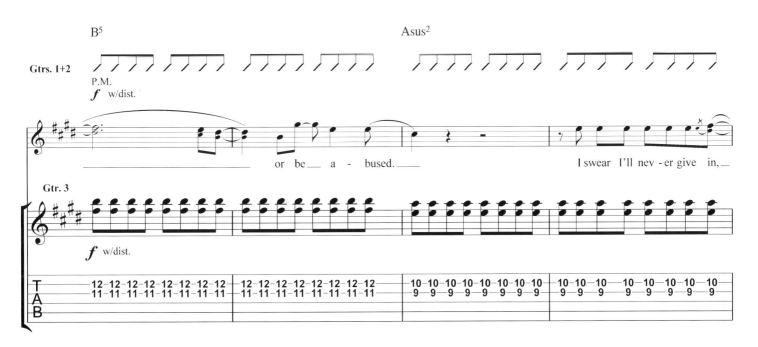

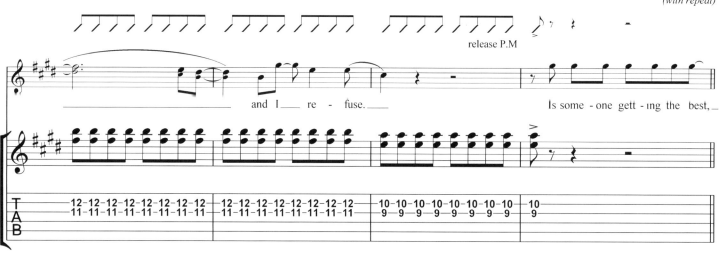

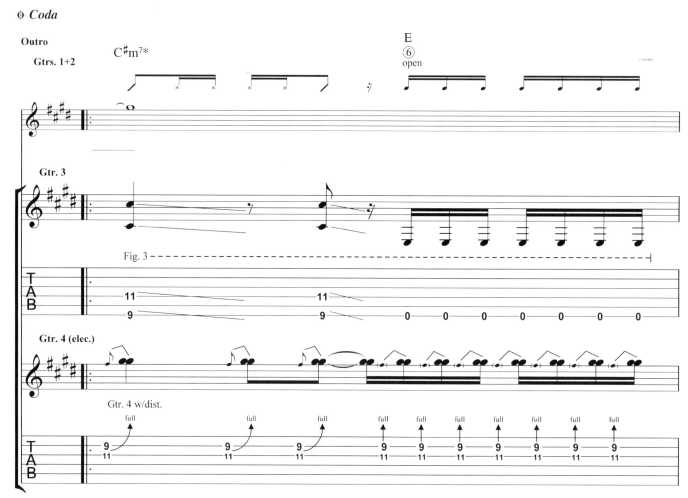

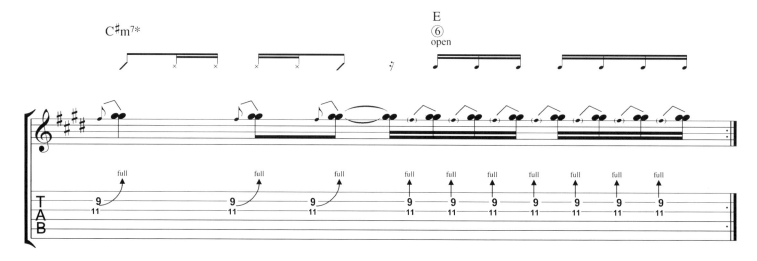

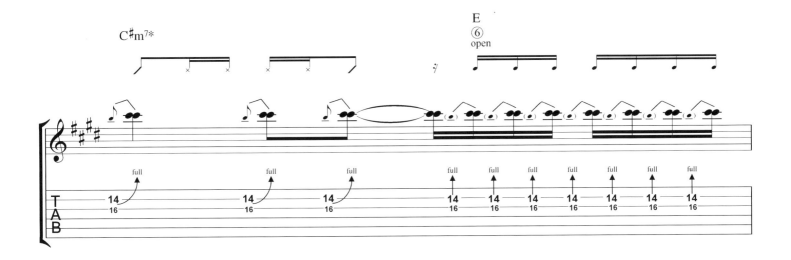

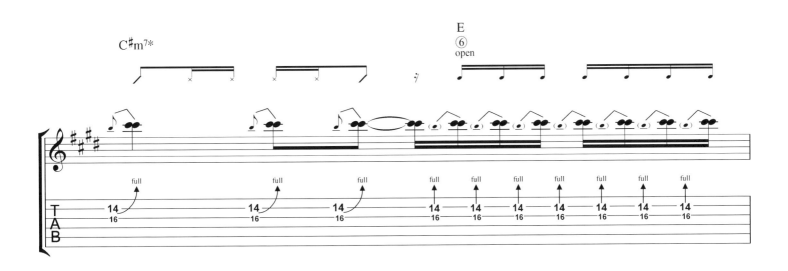

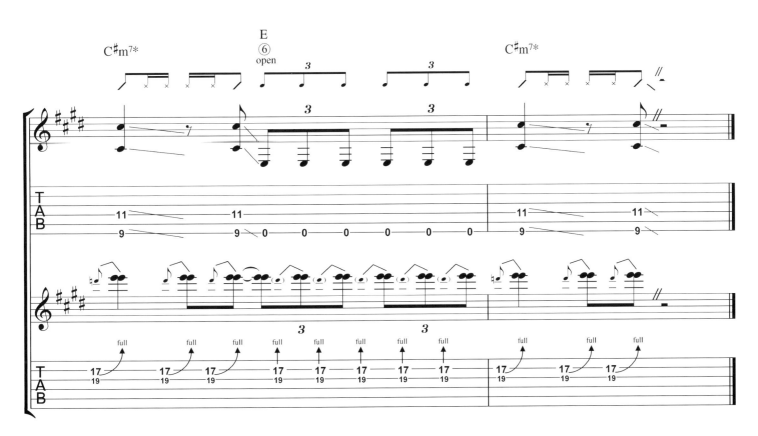

doa

Words & Music by
Dave Grohl, Taylor Hawkins, Nate Mendel & Chris Shiflett

Full performance demo: CD track 4
Backing only: CD track 11

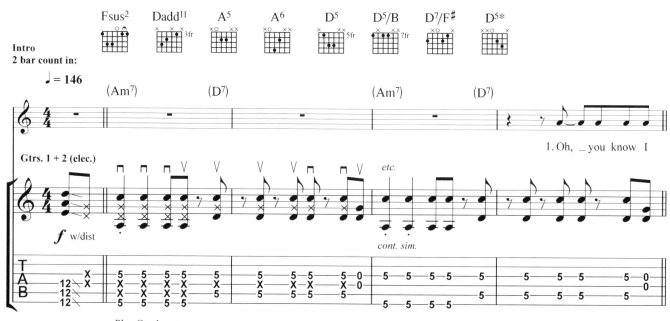

Intro
2 bar count in:

1. Oh, __ you know I

Play Gtr. 1 part

Verse

did it, it's ov-er and I feel fine. __ No-thing you can say is gon-na change my mind. Wait-
fin-ished, I'm get-ting you off my chest. Na-ture come clean in a dirt-y dress. A

-ed and I wait at the long-est night. Noth-ing like the taste of sweet
pro-mise is a pro-mise you kept __ in check. Hard __ to cross a heart that beats

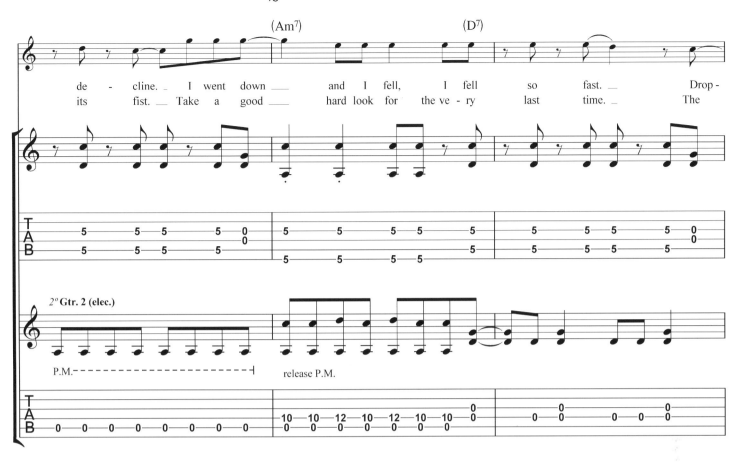

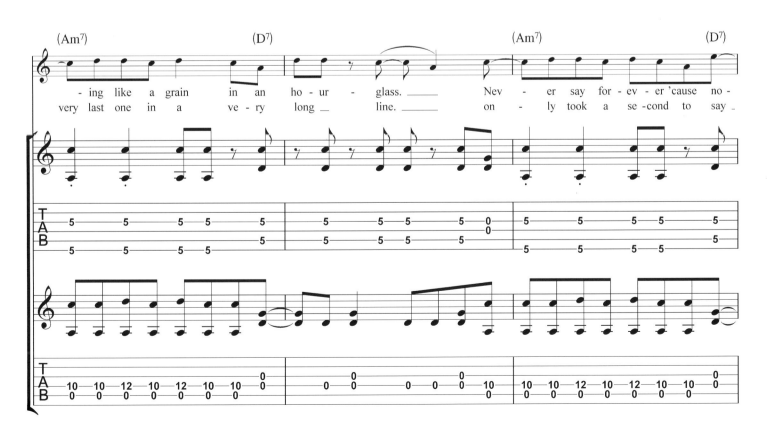

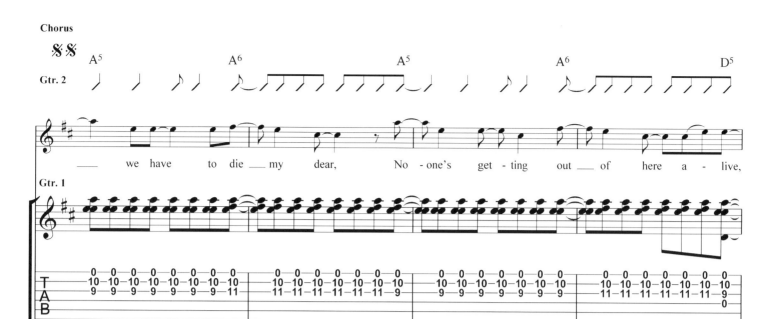

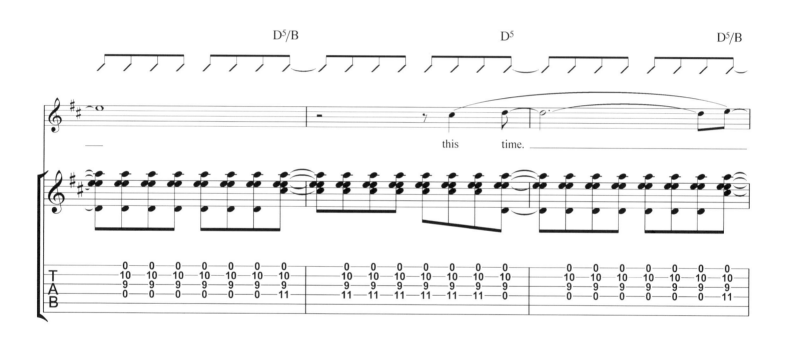

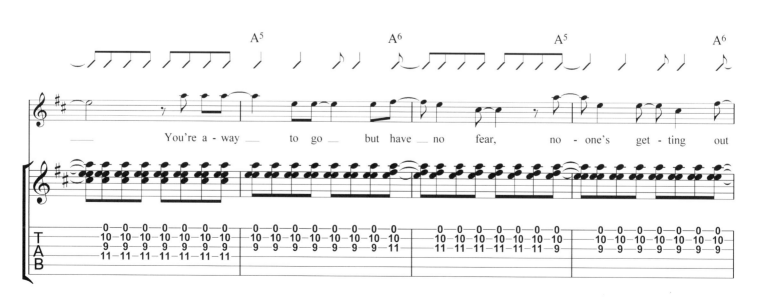

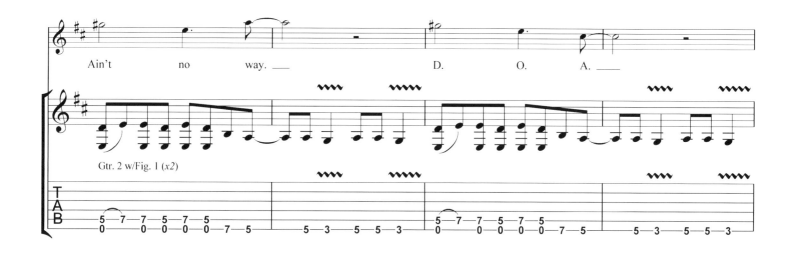

Ain't no way. D. O. A.

Gtr. 2 w/Fig. 1 (x2)

D.S. al Coda

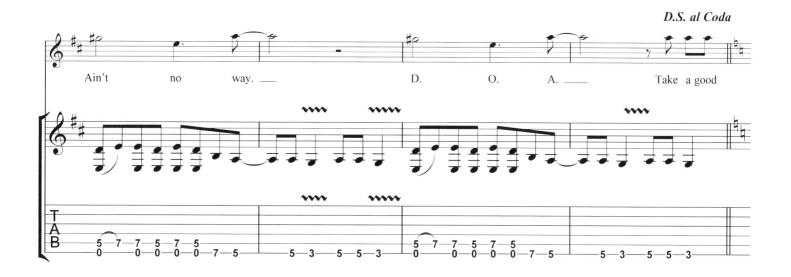

Ain't no way. D. O. A. Take a good

⊕ *Coda*

- er mind there's no - thing I can do.

Dadd¹¹

Gtrs. 1 + 2

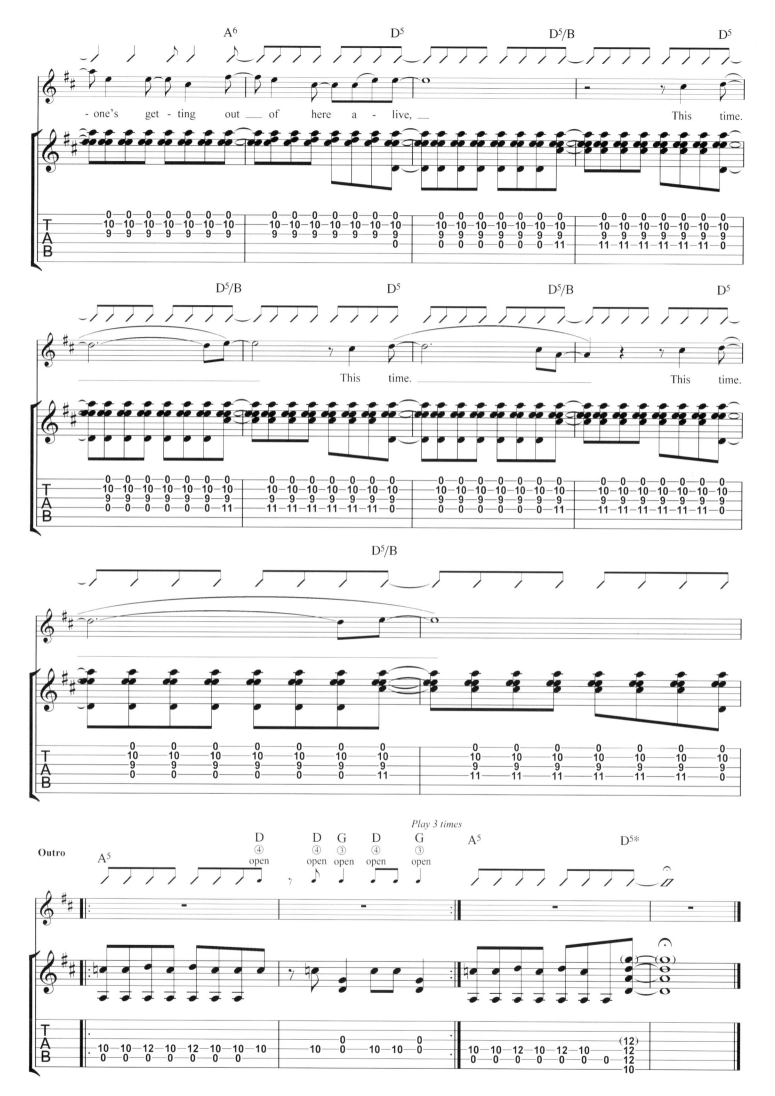

the pretender

Words & Music by
Dave Grohl, Taylor Hawkins, Nate Mendel & Chris Shiflett

Full performance demo: CD track 5
Backing only: CD track 12

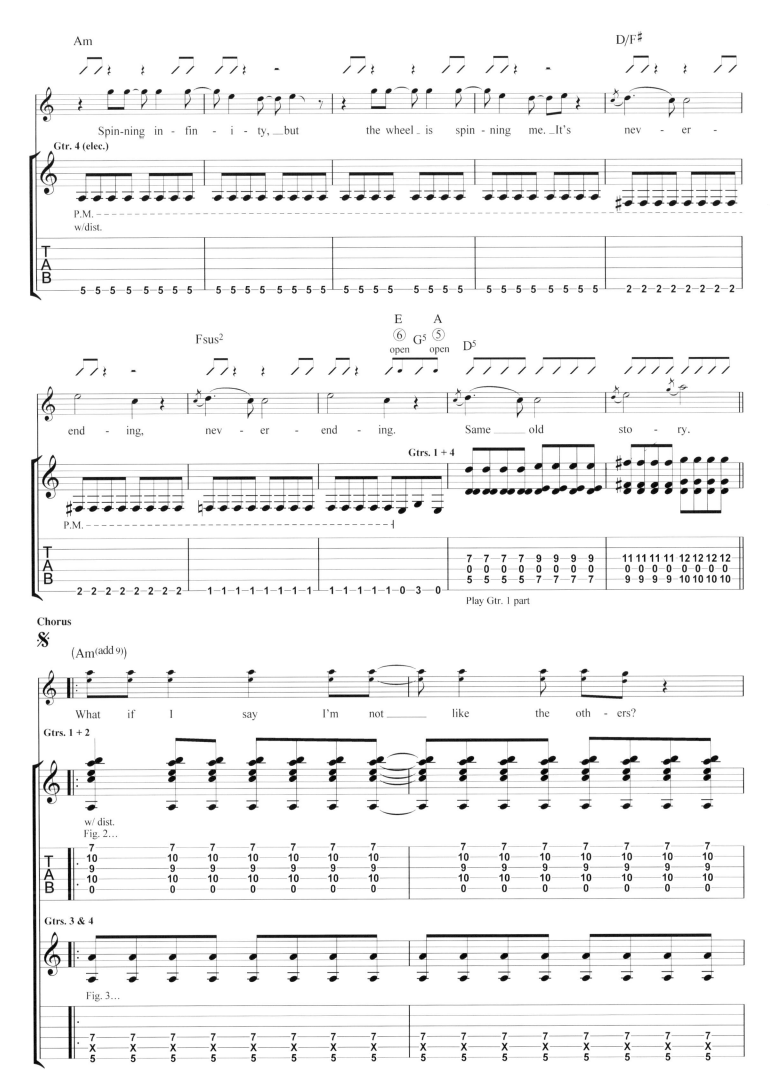

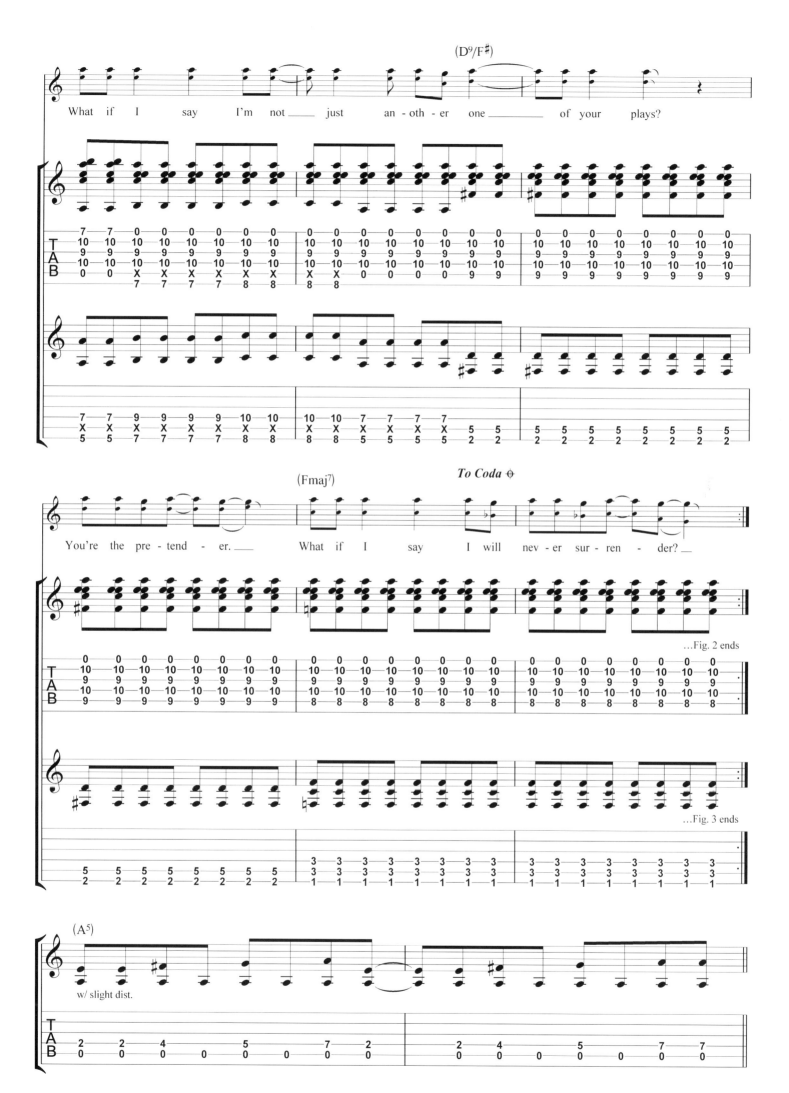

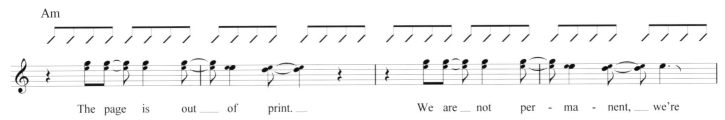

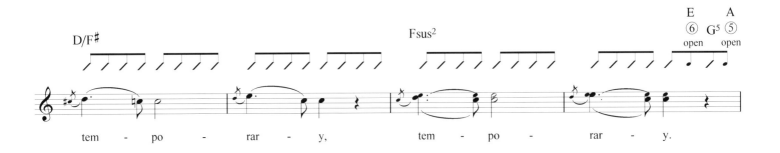

Interlude

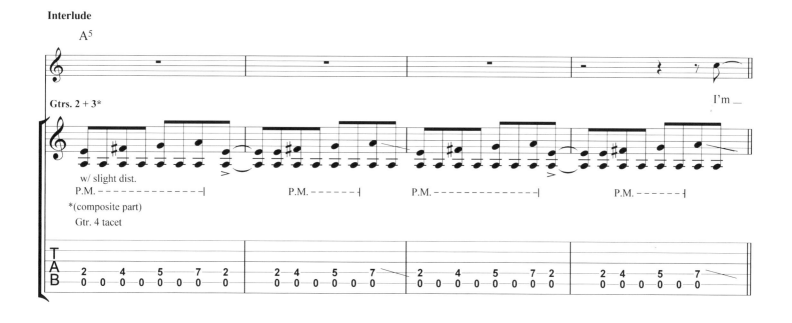

Bridge

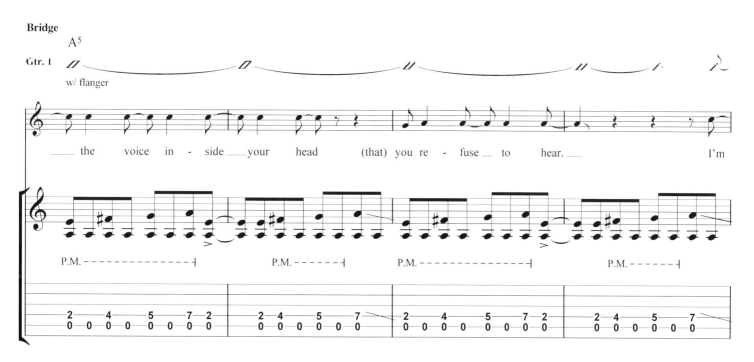

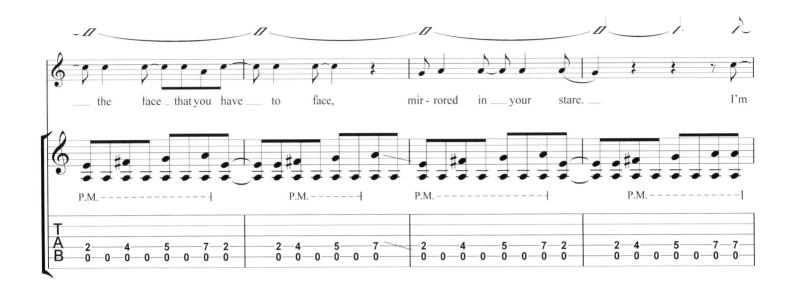

the face that you have to face, mir-rored in your stare. I'm

P.M. ---------------- | P.M. ------- | P.M. ------------- | P.M. ----------- |

Add **Gtr. 4** in ♪'s (A5)

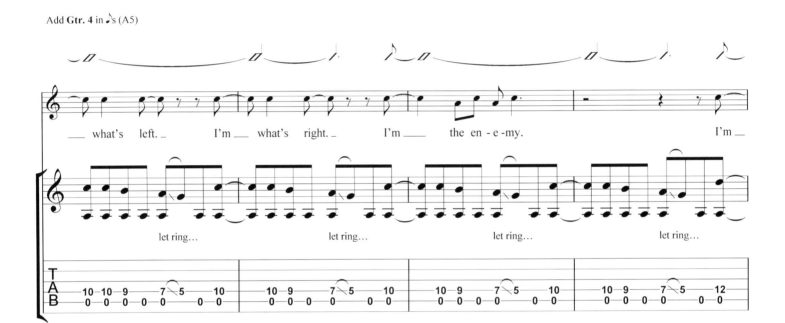

what's left. I'm what's right. I'm the en-e-my. I'm

let ring... let ring... let ring... let ring...

A⁵

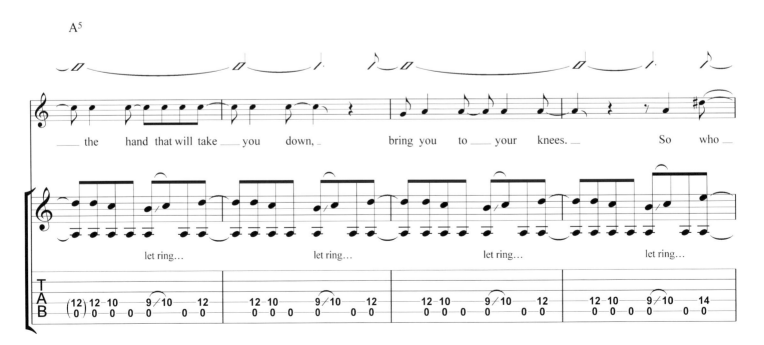

the hand that will take you down, bring you to your knees. So who

let ring... let ring... let ring... let ring...

Double tempo ♩ = 175

Chorus

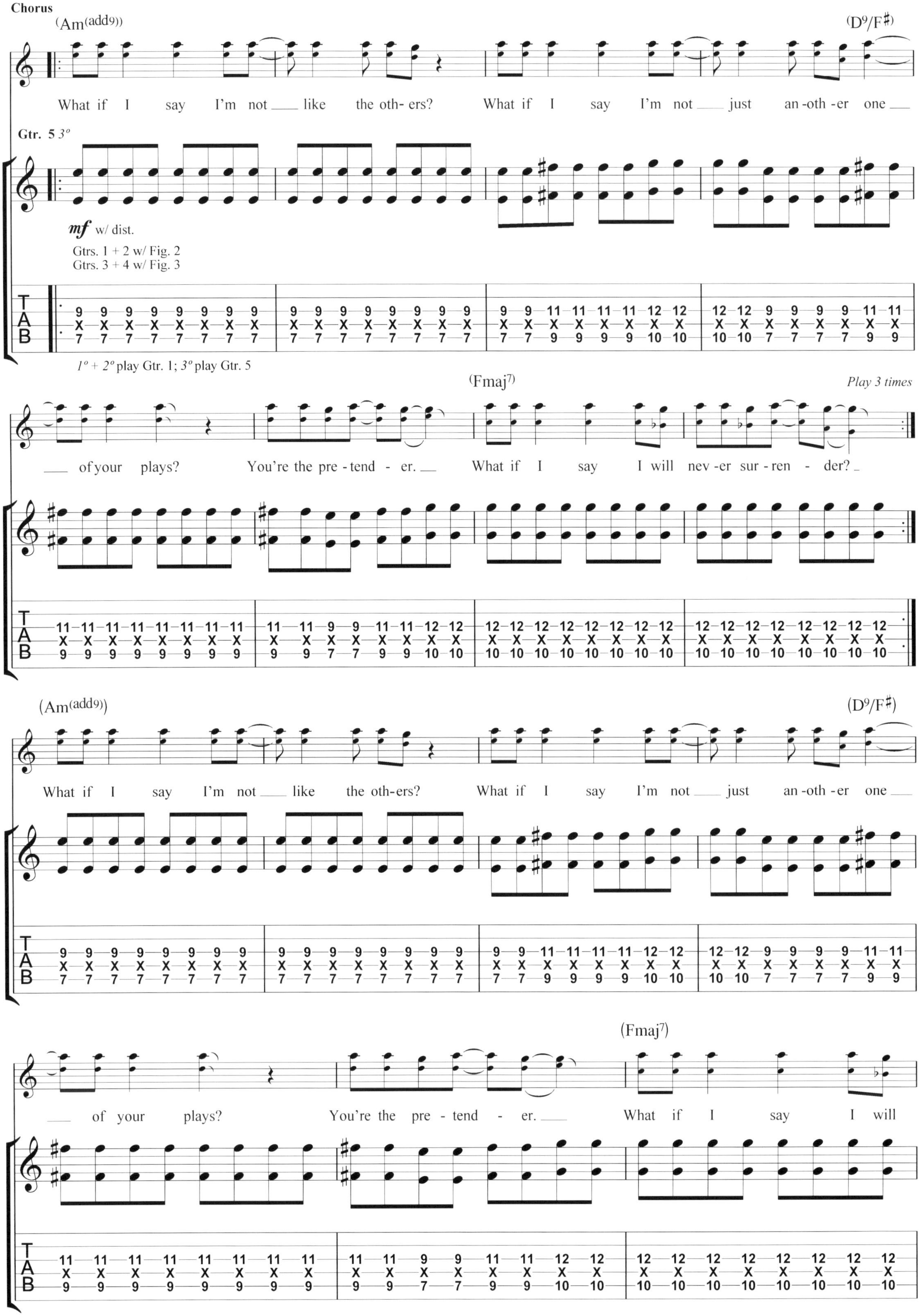

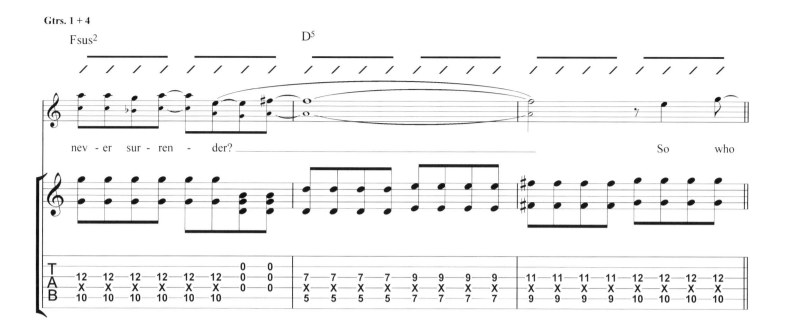

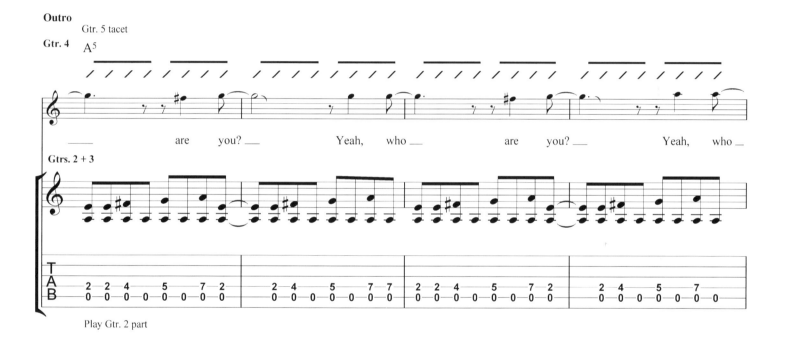

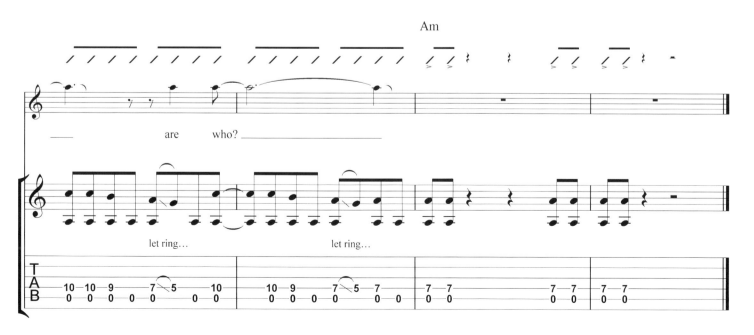

resolve

Words & Music by
Dave Grohl, Taylor Hawkins, Nate Mendel & Chris Shiflett

Full performance demo: CD track 6
Backing only: CD track 13

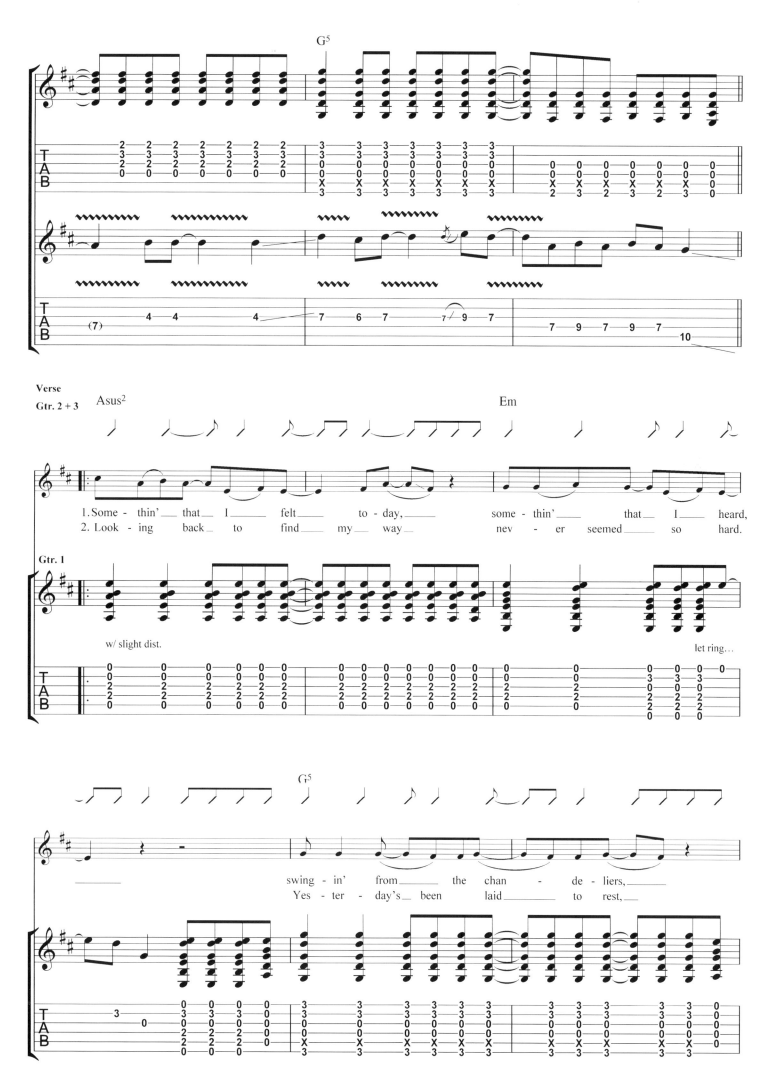

Verse
Gtr. 2 + 3

1. Some - thin' ___ that I ___ felt ___ to - day, ___ some - thin' ___ that I ___ heard,
2. Look - ing back to find ___ my way ___ nev - er seemed ___ so hard.

w/ slight dist.

let ring...

___ swing - in' from ___ the chan - de - liers, ___
Yes - ter - day's been laid to rest, ___

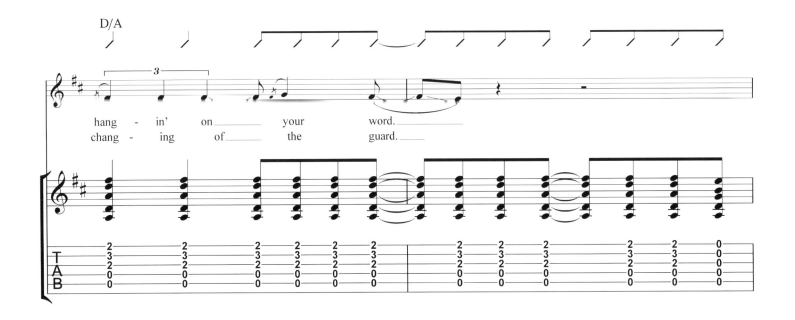

hang - in' on your word.
chang - ing of the guard.

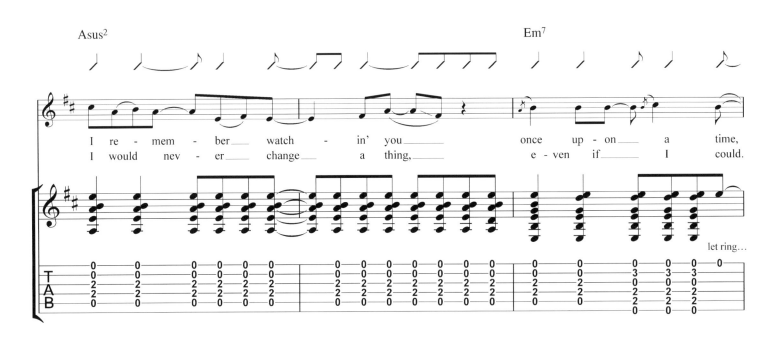

I re - mem - ber watch - in' you once up - on a time,
I would nev - er change a thing, e - ven if I could.

let ring...

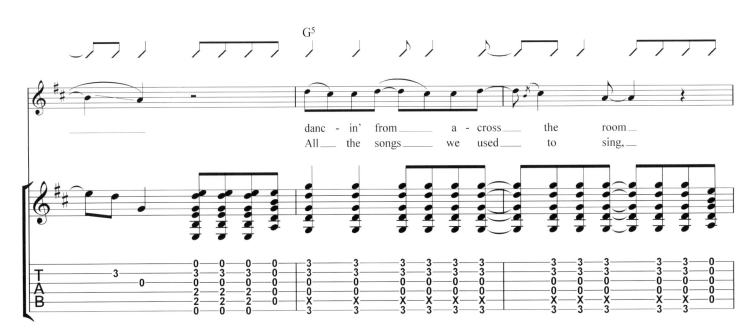

danc - in' from a - cross the room
All the songs we used to sing,

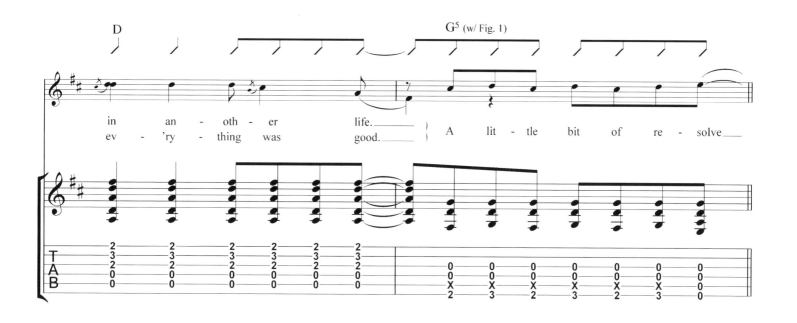

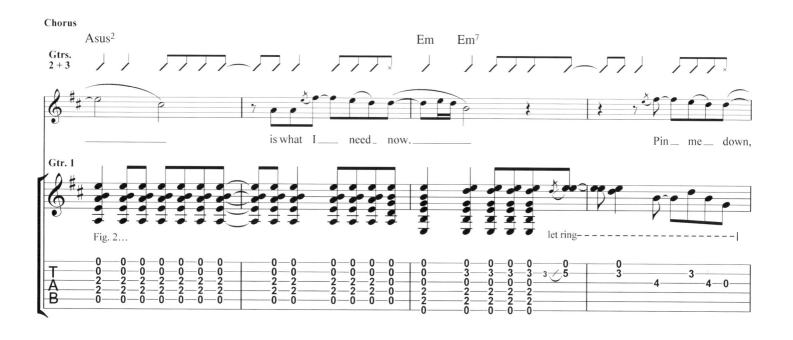

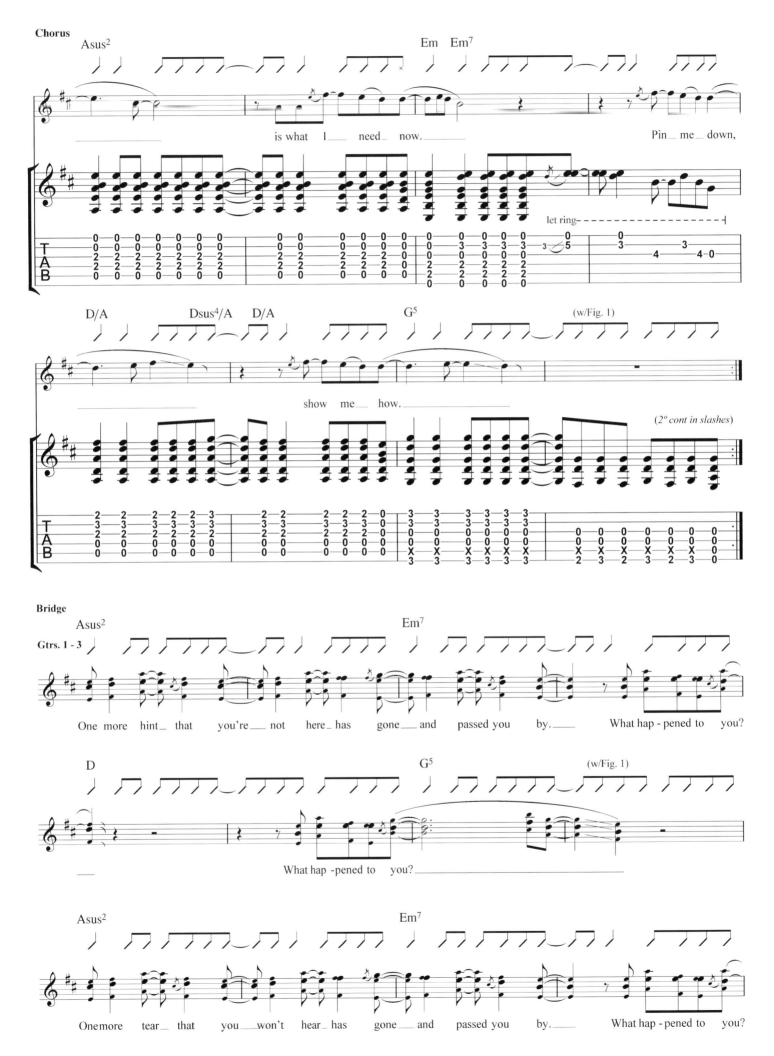

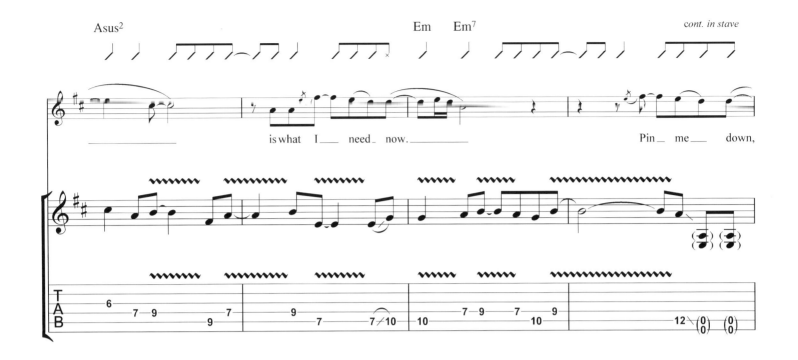

is what I____ need__ now._____   Pin__ me____ down,

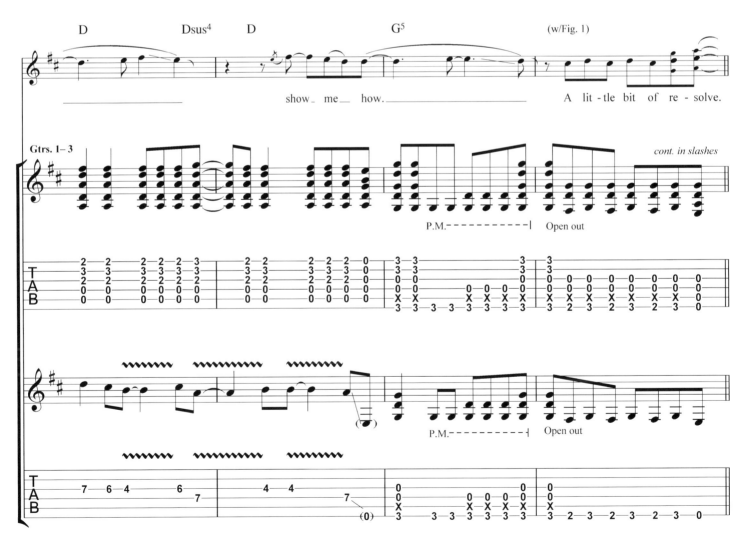

show__ me__ how._____   A lit‐tle bit of re‐solve.

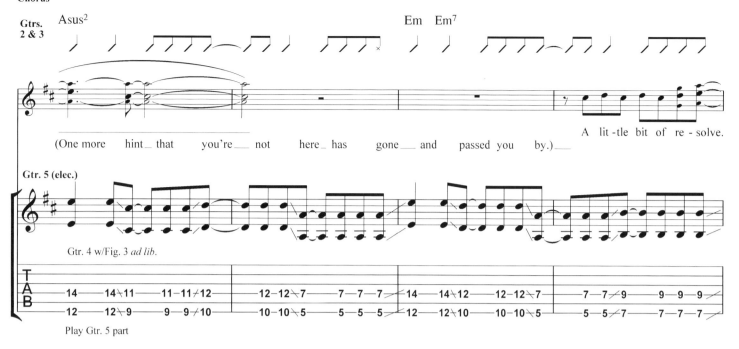

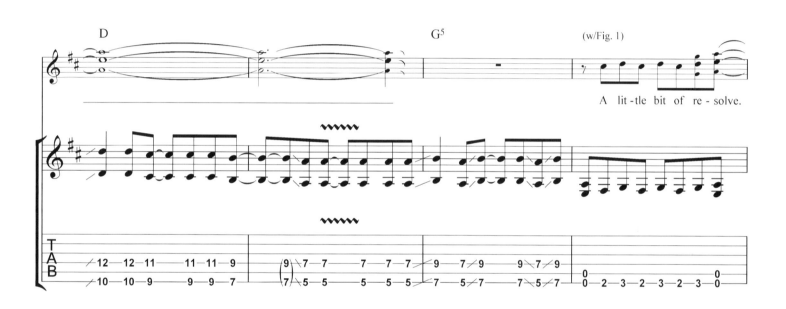

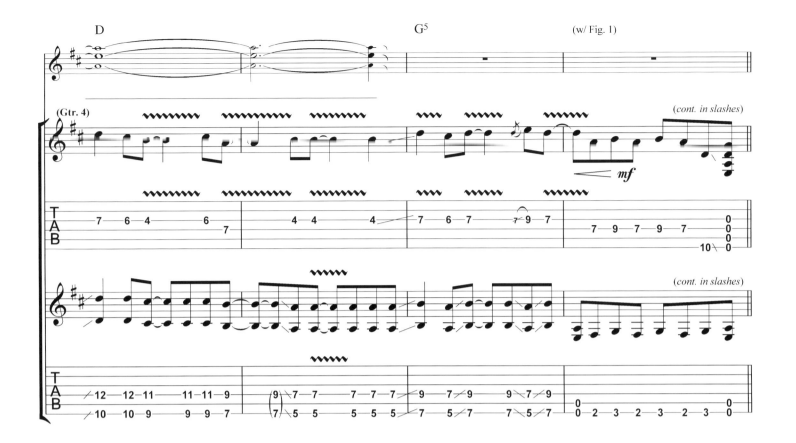

Free time

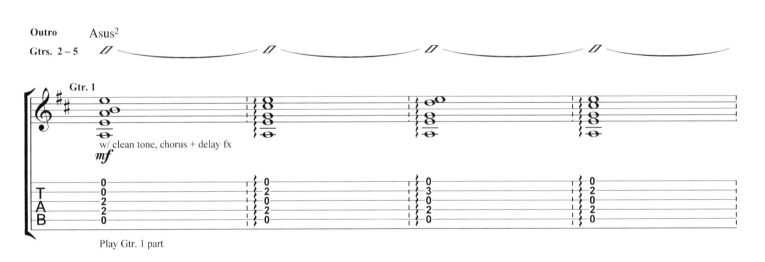

Play Gtr. 1 part

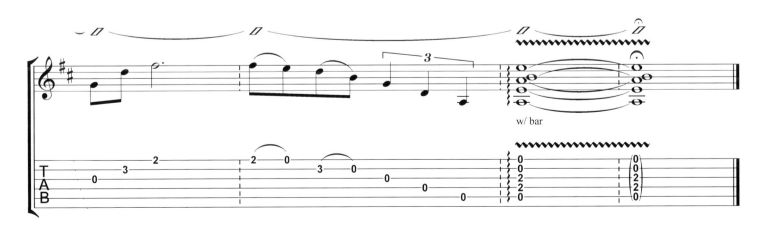

times like these

Words & Music by
Dave Grohl, Taylor Hawkins, Nate Mendel & Chris Shiflett

Full performance demo: CD track 7
Backing only: CD track 14

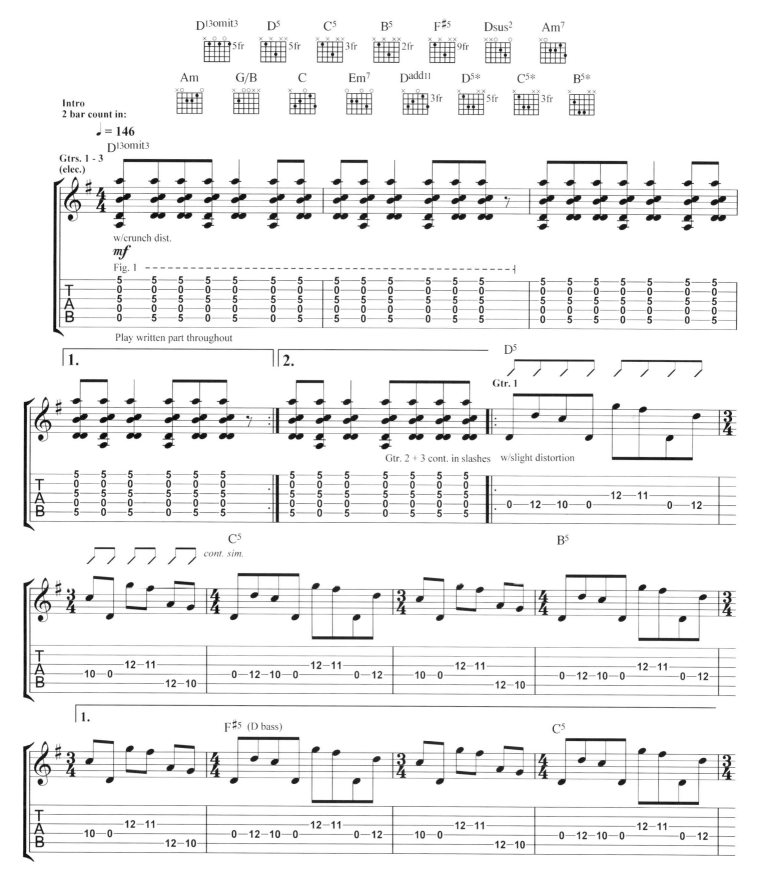

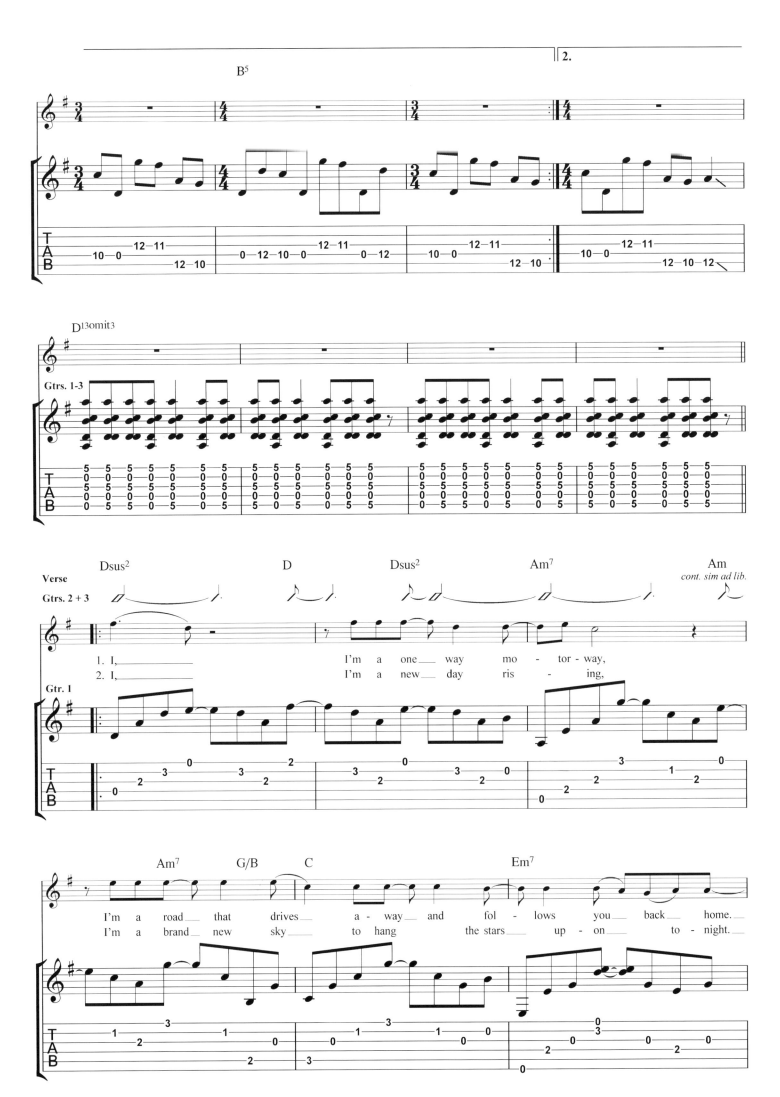

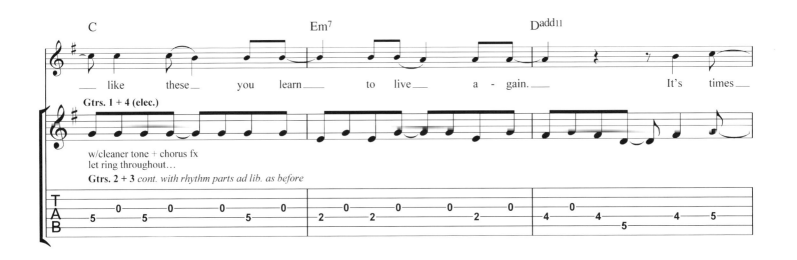

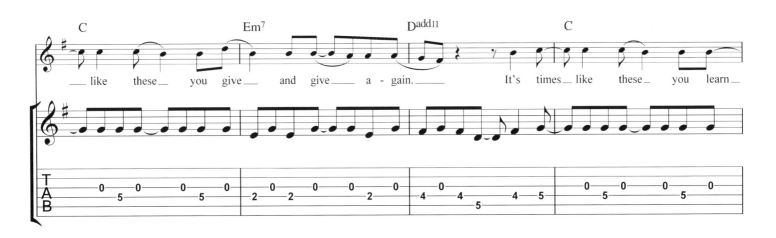

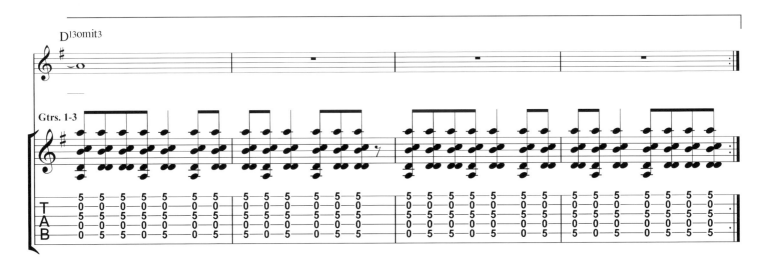

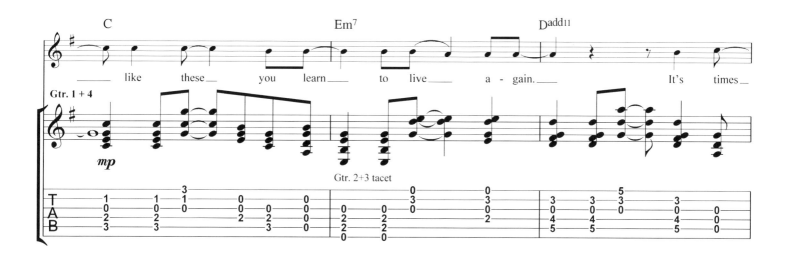

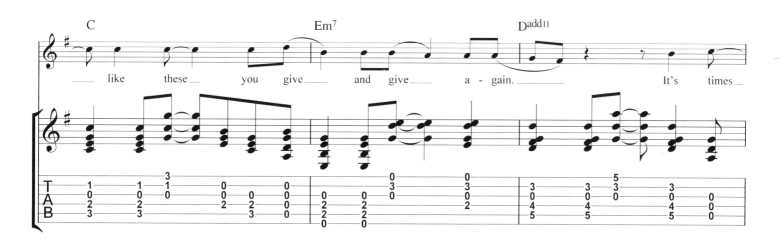

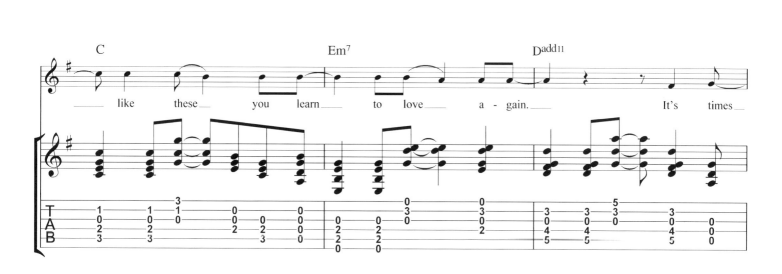

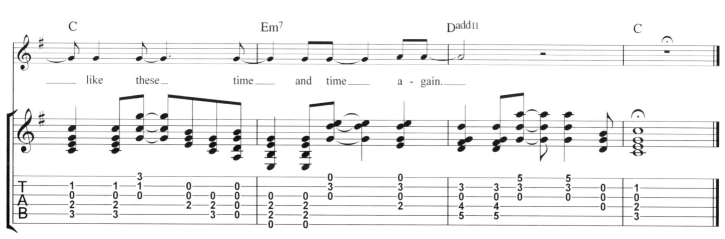

456789

CD track listing

Full instrumental performances (with guitar)...

1 all my life
(Grohl/Hawkins/Mendel/Shiflett)
EMI Virgin Music Limited/Universal/MCA Music Limited.

2 long road to ruin
(Grohl/Hawkins/Mendel/Shiflett)
Bug Music Limited/Universal/MCA Music Limited.

3 best of you
(Grohl/Hawkins/Mendel/Shiflett)
Bug Music Limited/Universal/MCA Music Limited.

4 doa
(Grohl/Hawkins/Mendel/Shiflett)
Bug Music Limited/Universal/MCA Music Limited.

5 the pretender
(Grohl/Hawkins/Mendel/Shiflett)
Bug Music Limited/Universal/MCA Music Limited.

6 resolve
(Grohl/Hawkins/Mendel/Shiflett)
Bug Music Limited/Universal/MCA Music Limited.

7 times like these
(Grohl/Hawkins/Mendel/Shiflett)
EMI Virgin Music Limited/Universal/MCA Music Limited.

Backing tracks only (without guitar)...

8 all my life

9 long road to ruin

10 best of you

11 doa

12 the pretender

13 resolve

14 times like these

> To remove your CD from the plastic sleeve, lift the small lip on the side to break the perforated flap. Replace the disc after use for convenient storage.

Published by

Wise Publications
14-15 Berners Street, London W1T 3LJ, UK

Exclusive Distributors:

Music Sales Limited
Distribution Centre, Newmarket Road,
Bury St Edmunds, Suffolk IP33 3YB, UK

Music Sales Pty Limited
20 Resolution Drive,
Caringbah, NSW 2229, Australia

Order No. AM994785
ISBN 978-1-84772-653-7
This book © Copyright 2008 Wise Publications,
a division of Music Sales Limited.

Printed in the EU

www.musicsales.com

Compiled by Nick Crispin
Music arranged by Arthur Dick
Edited by Tom Farncombe
Music processed by Paul Ewers Music Design

All Guitars by Arthur Dick
Bass by Paul Townsend
Drums by Brett Morgan

CD recorded, mixed and mastered by Jonas Persson

Your Guarantee of Quality
As publishers, we strive to produce every book
to the highest commercial standards.
The music has been freshly engraved and the book has
been carefully designed to minimise awkward page turns
and to make playing from it a real pleasure.
Particular care has been given to specifying acid-free,
neutral-sized paper made from pulps which have not been
elemental chlorine bleached. This pulp is from farmed
sustainable forests and was produced with special regard
for the environment.
Throughout, the printing and binding have been planned
to ensure a sturdy, attractive publication which should
give years of enjoyment.
If your copy fails to meet our high standards,
please inform us and we will gladly replace it.